THE TINIEST HIPPO

by Yvonne Winer

Illustrated by Donna Gynell

On Monday, the tiniest hippo said,
'Look, I'm covered in spots!'

The wise old hippos all nodded and winked.
'We think your spots are grand.'

'I tricked them,' thought the tiniest hippo and splashed back into the water.

On Tuesday, the tiniest hippo said,
'Look, I'm covered in stripes!'
The wise old hippos all nodded and winked.
'We think your stripes are grand.'

'I tricked them,' thought the tiniest hippo and splashed back into the water.

On Wednesday, the tiniest hippo said,
'Look, I'm covered in checks!'
The wise old hippos all nodded and winked.
'We think your checks are grand.'

'I tricked them,' thought the tiniest hippo and splashed back into the water.

On Thursday, the tiniest hippo said, 'Look!'

But the tiniest hippo saw no wise old hippo in sight.

'Where have all the hippos gone?'
asked the tiniest hippo.

'We were covered in water!'
called all the wise old hippos.

'You tricked me,' said the tiniest hippo.
'You tricked me!'

'Well what do you think of that?'
said the wise old hippos.

'I think your water is grand!'
said the tiniest hippo
and splashed them all.

Published by Era Publications,
220 Grange Road, Flinders Park, SA 5025 Australia

Text © Yvonne Winer, 1987
Illustrations © Donna Gynell, 1987
Printed in Hong Kong
First published 1987

**National Library of Australia
Cataloguing-in-Publication Data:**
Winer, Yvonne, 1934-   .
    The tiniest hippo.

    ISBN 0 908507 67 4.

    1. Hippopotamus — Juvenile fiction.
    I. Gynell, Donna, 1960-   .
    II. Title. (Series : Magic bean).

A823'.3

For worldwide distribution details of
this book see Era Publications' website:
http://www.era-publications.com.au

15   14   13   12   11   10   9   8   7   6   5